The
Chatto & Windus
Almanack

Stanley Spencer was born on 30 June 1891 at Cookham, Berks. Between 1908 and 1912 he studied at the Slade School, where his contemporaries included Mark Gertler, William Roberts and Paul Nash. After war service with the R.A.M.C. in Macedonia he returned to England and embarked on the work that was to make him one of the greatest of 20th-century English painters. Between 1927 and 1932 he worked on the decorations for the Sandham Memorial Chapel, Burghclere, later presented to the National Trust. He was elected in 1932 to the Royal Academy, but resigned two years later in protest over the rejection of 'St Francis and the Birds'. During World War 2 he was commissioned by the War Artists' Advisory Committee to paint pictures of shipyards. Spencer rejoined the Royal Academy in 1950 and was elected R.A.; he was knighted in 1958. He died on 14 December 1959.

The
Chatto & Windus
Almanack

With designs by

STANLEY SPENCER

CHATTO & WINDUS

THE HOGARTH PRESS

LONDON

First published in 1926 by Chatto & Windus

This edition published in 1983 by
Chatto & Windus · The Hogarth Press
40 William IV St, London WC2N 4DF

British Library Cataloguing in Publication Data

The Chatto & Windus almanack.
1. Spencer, Stanley
1. Spencer, Stanley
741.942   NC431.s/
ISBN 0-7011-3914-5

Printed in Great Britain by
Redwood Burn Ltd
Trowbridge, Wiltshire

Publisher's Note

Some time early in 1926, Charles Prentice of Chatto & Windus commissioned Stanley Spencer to produce twenty-five pen-and-ink drawings on domestic and pastoral themes for *A Chatto & Windus Almanack for 1927*. This was the second such *Almanack*; the previous year's had been illustrated by Albert Rutherston, with a bookplate by Gordon Craig and contributions by Lytton Strachey, Arnold Bennett, C. E. Montague, Aldous Huxley and David Garnett. It was published in an Ordinary Edition at 1s., with a small Edition de Luxe which was, as the catalogue said, 'immediately snapped up by interested bibliophiles'.

As is so often the case, the precise details of how and why Spencer was approached do not appear in the files. Clearly the art of commissioning by telephone was already well advanced. The first letter from Prentice to Spencer is dated 6 April 1926, inquiring gently about Spencer's progress. Spencer replied on 10 May, saying that he had done all but two of the upright drawings (out of twelve, one for each month) and four of the others (also out of twelve; the twenty-fifth was to be a version of the traditional Chatto twins, to be used on the cover and on the title page). He expected to be finished within a fortnight. Oddly, Spencer did not at this stage appear even to know Prentice's initials, let alone his Christian name; his postcard is addressed to '– Prentice, Esq'.

No formal letter of agreement was exchanged until 9 June. Chatto paid Spencer £30, in return for the right to use the drawings once only, in the *Almanack*. Ownership of the drawings themselves and all other rights remained with Spencer.

June and July were spent proofing and re-proofing the drawings. For this purpose, Spencer was handed over to a Mr Whitworth, 'whose knowledge', Prentice wrote modestly, 'of what engravers can and cannot do is incomparably greater than mine'. A further £2 was paid to Spencer on 26 July on account of damage to the April drawing of two girls handing a bunch of tulips over a hedge; whatever the damage was, it seems not to have got in the way of adequate reproduction.

By October, when the *Almanack* was published, Spencer was living at Wangford, near Lowestoft (where he and Hilda Carline had been married in 1925), doing 'two nice "fat" landscapes', and otherwise kicking his heels 'waiting for the "Chapel" to be finished'. He pronounced himself pleased with both editions of the *Almanack*: 'I think that they are all that could be desired; I was much taken with the proportion; the "de Luxe" lids [*sic:* did he mean boards?] and especially the type, small but clear. I like the green covers and I like the feel of the paper ... the whole get-up is in keeping with the drawings.' Spencer's Chatto twins were reproduced in the *T.L.S.* during the week of publication. He asked the village newsagent to reserve him a copy: 'He looked very dubious and said he would try.' In the event Spencer got his *Times*, but it contained no supplement.

Prentice wrote to Spencer on 22 October expressing pleasure at his verdict, but rather glumly reporting on the book's progress: 'The little book, as you may guess, has met with a very mixed reception: some people entranced with it, and others (the majority, I'm afraid) disliking it intensely. But these things are always so.' It is hard at this stage to see just why the majority should be so ungrateful or indeed to understand Prentice's apparent resignation. It is possible that Prentice had felt that he was taking something of a gamble on Spencer (whose first one-man show was not to be held until the spring of 1927), but the reviews, although not extensive, were uniformly favourable. The *Observer* described the drawings as 'impish and attractive', adding that 'the smooth pages make one's pen champ to be at them'. The *Burlington Magazine* called the *Almanack* 'quite charming', while the *Oxford Magazine* said, 'very delightful . . . makes the most pleasing of engagement books'.

In any case, sales of the *Almanack* did not fall far short of Chatto's expectations. It was published in an edition of 3,000 at 1s., bound in paper covers; 250 copies of the Edition de Luxe were issued at 10s. 6d; all were printed by the Curwen Press. 2,750 of the cheaper edition were sold, the remainder being used for 'packing' early in 1928. The Edition de Luxe was no doubt snapped up the same 'interested bibliophiles'. Sadly, no copy of the latter remains on the Chatto file; it was clearly, to judge by the relative cost of producing it, a handsome volume. A further *Almanack* was promised for 1928, 'to. be planned on different lines'; it never appeared.

Two copies of the *Almanack*, annotated in Spencer's hand, are held in the Tate Gallery archives. Several of the drawings in them have been squared up for development into major paintings. July's drawing of Hilda Carline smelling a flower, for example, he introduced with very little alteration into 'The Resurrection, Cookham' (or perhaps the other way round, since the painting was finished in March 1926). August's drawing of Hilda reading in a haystack to an audience of ducks and hens became an important component of the controversial 'St Francis and the Birds'.

In the belief that this little book, the only one Spencer ever illustrated, is far too delightful and valuable to be consigned to oblivion, Chatto & Windus have great pleasure in reissuing it now. Internally it is identical with the original edition with two exceptions; a List of Recent Books has been removed from the end, and the days of the week which related to 1927 have been deleted so as to make the *Almanack* applicable to any year. Finally, we would like to thank Shirin and Unity Spencer, Stanley Spencer's daughters and executrices, for their permission to use the drawings once again, and Dr J. A. Edwards of the University of Reading for his help in uncovering files and other material.

Mike Petty
Chatto & Windus Ltd   August 1983

The Almanack

JANUARY

JANUARY 1*st*

JANUARY 2

JANUARY 3

JANUARY 4

JANUARY 5

JANUARY 6

JANUARY 7

JANUARY 8

JANUARY 9

JANUARY 10

JANUARY 11

JANUARY 12

JANUARY 13

JANUARY 14

JANUARY 15

JANUARY 16

JANUARY 17

JANUARY 18

JANUARY 19

JANUARY 20

JANUARY 21

JANUARY 22

JANUARY 23

JANUARY 24

JANUARY 25

JANUARY 26

JANUARY 27

JANUARY 28

JANUARY 29

JANUARY 30

JANUARY 31

FEBRUARY

FEBRUARY 1st

FEBRUARY 2

FEBRUARY 3

FEBRUARY 4

FEBRUARY 5

FEBRUARY 6

FEBRUARY 7

FEBRUARY 8

FEBRUARY 9

FEBRUARY 10

FEBRUARY 11

FEBRUARY 12

FEBRUARY 13

FEBRUARY 14

FEBRUARY 15

FEBRUARY 16

FEBRUARY 17

FEBRUARY 18

FEBRUARY 19

FEBRUARY 20

FEBRUARY 21

FEBRUARY 22

FEBRUARY 23

FEBRUARY 24

FEBRUARY 25

FEBRUARY 26

FEBRUARY 27

FEBRUARY 28

FEBRUARY 29

MARCH

MARCH 1st

MARCH 2

MARCH 3

MARCH 4

MARCH 5

MARCH 6

MARCH 7

MARCH 8

MARCH 9

MARCH 10

MARCH 11

MARCH I 2

MARCH I 3

MARCH I 4

MARCH 15

MARCH 16

MARCH 17

MARCH 18

MARCH 19

MARCH 20

.

MARCH 21

MARCH 22

MARCH 23

MARCH 24

MARCH 25

MARCH 26

MARCH 27

MARCH 28

MARCH 29

MARCH 30

MARCH 31

APRIL

APRIL 1*st*

APRIL 2

APRIL 3

APRIL 4

APRIL 5

APRIL 6

APRIL 7

APRIL 8

APRIL 9

APRIL 10

APRIL 11

APRIL 12

APRIL 13

APRIL 14

APRIL 15

APRIL 16

APRIL 17

APRIL 18

APRIL 19

APRIL 20

APRIL 21

APRIL 22

APRIL 23

APRIL 24

APRIL 25

APRIL 26

APRIL 27

APRIL 28

APRIL 29

APRIL 30

MAY

MAY 1st

MAY 2

MAY 3

MAY 4

MAY 5

MAY 6

MAY 7

MAY 8

MAY 9

MAY 10

MAY 11

MAY 12

MAY 13

MAY 14

MAY 15

MAY 16

MAY 17

MAY 18

MAY 19

MAY 20

MAY 21

MAY 22

MAY 23

MAY 24

MAY 25

MAY 26

MAY 27

MAY 28

MAY 29

MAY 30

MAY 31

JUNE

JUNE 1*st*

JUNE 2

JUNE 3

JUNE 4

JUNE 5

JUNE 6

JUNE 7

JUNE 8

JUNE 9

JUNE 10

JUNE 11

JUNE 12

JUNE 13

JUNE 14

JUNE 15

JUNE 16

JUNE 17

JUNE 18

JUNE 19

JUNE 20

JUNE 21

JUNE 22

JUNE 23

JUNE 24

JUNE 25

JUNE 26

JUNE 27

JUNE 28

JUNE 29

JUNE 30

JULY

JULY 1st

JULY 2

JULY 3

JULY 4

JULY 5

JULY 6

JULY 7

JULY 8

JULY 9

JULY 10

JULY 11

JULY 12

JULY 13

JULY 14

JULY 15

JULY 16

JULY 17

JULY 18

JULY 19

JULY 20

JULY 21

JULY 22

JULY 23

JULY 24

JULY 25

JULY 26

JULY 27

JULY 28

JULY 29

JULY 30

JULY 31

AUGUST

AUGUST 1st

AUGUST 2

AUGUST 3

AUGUST 4

AUGUST 5

AUGUST 6

AUGUST 7

AUGUST 8

AUGUST 9

AUGUST 10

AUGUST 11

AUGUST 12

AUGUST 13

AUGUST 14

AUGUST 15

AUGUST 16

AUGUST 17

AUGUST 18

AUGUST 19

AUGUST 20

AUGUST 21

AUGUST 22

AUGUST 23

AUGUST 24

AUGUST 25

AUGUST 26

AUGUST 27

AUGUST 28

AUGUST 29

AUGUST 30

AUGUST 31

SEPTEMBER

SEPTEMBER 1st

SEPTEMBER 2

SEPTEMBER 3

SEPTEMBER 4

SEPTEMBER 5

SEPTEMBER 6

SEPTEMBER 7

SEPTEMBER 8

SEPTEMBER 9

SEPTEMBER 10

SEPTEMBER 11

SEPTEMBER 12

SEPTEMBER 13

SEPTEMBER 14

SEPTEMBER 15

SEPTEMBER 16

SEPTEMBER 17

SEPTEMBER 18

SEPTEMBER 19

SEPTEMBER 20

SEPTEMBER 21

SEPTEMBER 22

SEPTEMBER 23

SEPTEMBER 24

SEPTEMBER 25

SEPTEMBER 26

SEPTEMBER 27

SEPTEMBER 28

SEPTEMBER 29

OCTOBER

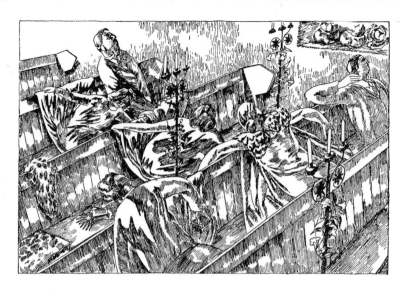

OCTOBER 1st

OCTOBER 2

OCTOBER 3

OCTOBER 4

OCTOBER 5

OCTOBER 6

OCTOBER 7

OCTOBER 8

OCTOBER 9

OCTOBER 10

OCTOBER 11

OCTOBER 12

OCTOBER 13

OCTOBER 14

OCTOBER 15

OCTOBER 16

OCTOBER 17

OCTOBER 18

OCTOBER 19

OCTOBER 20

OCTOBER 21

OCTOBER 22

OCTOBER 23

OCTOBER 24

OCTOBER 25

OCTOBER 26

OCTOBER 27

OCTOBER 28

OCTOBER 29

OCTOBER 30

OCTOBER 31

NOVEMBER

NOVEMBER 1<i>st</i>

NOVEMBER 2

NOVEMBER 3

NOVEMBER 4

NOVEMBER 5

NOVEMBER 6

NOVEMBER 7

NOVEMBER 8

NOVEMBER 9

NOVEMBER 10

NOVEMBER 11

NOVEMBER 12

NOVEMBER 13

NOVEMBER 14

NOVEMBER 15

NOVEMBER 16

NOVEMBER 17

NOVEMBER 18

NOVEMBER 19

NOVEMBER 20

NOVEMBER 21

NOVEMBER 22

NOVEMBER 23

NOVEMBER 24

NOVEMBER 25

NOVEMBER 26

NOVEMBER 27

NOVEMBER 28

NOVEMBER 29

NOVEMBER 30

DECEMBER

DECEMBER 1st

DECEMBER 2

DECEMBER 3

DECEMBER 4

DECEMBER 5

DECEMBER 6

DECEMBER 7

DECEMBER 8

DECEMBER 9

DECEMBER 10

DECEMBER 11

DECEMBER 12

DECEMBER 13

DECEMBER 14

DECEMBER 15

DECEMBER 16

DECEMBER 17

DECEMBER 18

DECEMBER 19

DECEMBER 20

DECEMBER 21

DECEMBER 22

DECEMBER 23

DECEMBER 24

DECEMBER 25

DECEMBER 26

DECEMBER 27

DECEMBER 28

DECEMBER 29